The Good-Companion Books

Nick and Dick

BY

Arthur I. Gates
Franklin T. Baker
AND
Celeste Comegys Peardon

ILLUSTRATED BY
FLORENCE McANELLY

NEW YORK
THE MACMILLAN COMPANY
1937

Set up and electrotyped. Published January, 1936
Reprinted August, 1936; January, 1937; June, 1937.

Contents

Chapter One—*In the City*

Chapter Two—*Fun in the City*

Chapter Three—*The Farm*

Chapter Four—*Fun at the Farm*

Chapter Five—*Home and School*

CHAPTER ONE
In the City

1

Nick and Dick

The Twins

The boys are Nick and Dick.

Nick and Dick are twins.

Some twins look just alike.
Nick and Dick look just alike.

One twin has a red suit.
Nick has the red suit.

One twin has a blue suit.
This twin is Dick.

A Street in a City

The twins live in a city.
This is a street in the city.
The twins live on this street.

This big brown house
is on a street in the city.
Nick and Dick
live on this street.
They live
in the big brown house

The twins live at the top
of the big brown house.
They look down
at the street.
They look down
at the tops of houses.

Nick and Dick look down
at the city streets.

They can see automobiles
on the streets.

They can see people
on the streets.

The Automobiles

Automobiles go up and down the city streets.

"Honk! Honk!"

"Toot! Toot!"

Up and down they go!

11

There are red and green lights
on the city streets.

The red and green lights
are for the people
and the automobiles.

The red light says
to the people
and the automobiles,
"Stop! Stop! Stop!"

The green light says
to the people
and the automobiles,
"Go! Go! Go!"

The Elevator

Nick and Dick
ride to the top
of the big brown house.

They ride to the top
of the big brown house
in the elevator.

Ben is the elevator boy.
He likes to give the twins
a ride in the elevator.

The twins like to ride
in the elevator.

15

Nick says, "I like to ride
in the elevator.
I like going up.
It is fun to go up, up, up."

Dick says, "I like to ride
in the elevator.
I like going down.
It is fun
to go down, down, down."

16

Which Is Right?

1. Nick and Ben are twins.
   Nick and Dick are twins.

2. Nick has on a blue suit.
   Dick has on a blue suit.

3. Dick has on a red suit.
   Nick has on a red suit.

4. The twins live
in a brown house.
   The twins live
in a blue house.

5. Ben is the elevator boy.
   Dick is the elevator boy.

Which Is Right?

1. "Stop! Stop! Stop!"
   says the green light
   says the red light

2. "Honk! Honk! Toot! Toot!"
   says the automobile
   says the elevator

3. "It is fun
to go up, up, up," says,
   Nick   Dick   Ben

4. "It is fun
to go down, down, down," says,
   Ben   Nick   Dick

18

CHAPTER TWO
Fun in the City

The Store

Going to the Store

"I am going to the store," said Mother.

"May I go, Mother?" said Nick.

"May I go, Mother?" said Dick.

"Yes," said Mother,
"you may go to the store."

Mother and the twins
went down, down, down
in the elevator to the street.

The Policeman

On the street
was a policeman.

"Good morning, boys,"
said the policeman.

"Good morning!"
said the twins.

23

"We are going
to cross the street," said Dick.

"We are going to the store,"
said Nick.

The policeman said,
"When you see the green light,
you may cross the street!"

Mother saw the green light.
The twins saw the green light.
They saw the automobiles stop.

"There is the green light!"
said Nick and Dick.

"You may cross the street,"
said the policeman.

24

The Storekeeper

Nick and Dick and Mother
went to a store.

"Good morning, boys,"
said the storekeeper.
"What are you going to buy
this morning?"

"I am going to buy
some milk," said Nick.

"I am going to buy
some bread," said Dick.

"I am going to buy
some eggs," said Mother.

Nick brought home the milk.
Dick brought home the bread.
Mother brought home the eggs.
Mother and the twins
went up, up, up
in the elevator.

They went up, up, up
right to the top
of the big brown house.

Then they were at home!

Going to the Park

One morning Nick said,
"Please, may we go
to the park, Father?"

"Yes," said Father,
"you and Dick and I
will go to the park."

Father and the twins
rode to the park
on a big green bus.
They sat high up
on the top of the bus.

29

"I can see streets
and automobiles
from the top of the bus,"
said Nick.

"I can see people and houses
from the top of the bus,"
said Dick.

"I can see
a big, big, big city
from the top of the bus,"
said Father.

"I can see the park,"
said Nick.
"I can see green grass."

In the Park

Father and the twins sat down
on the green grass in the park.

Father had brought some dinner
in a box.

It was fun to eat dinner
in the park.

The twins saw
a balloon man in the park.
He had red and blue
and green balloons.
Father let the twins
buy two pretty balloons.
Nick had a red balloon.
Dick had a blue balloon.

Nick and Dick
looked for a peanut man.

"Peanuts! Peanuts!
Buy some peanuts!"
said the peanut man.

Father let the twins
buy some peanuts.
It was fun
to eat peanuts in the park.

Nick and Dick played
in the park.

They ran up and down.

They played with the balloons.

They ran and played
on the green grass.

Then Father said,
"It is time to go home."

"Are we going home
on a green bus?" said Dick.

"Yes," said Father.

The twins and Father
went home on a green bus.

The bus said,
"Toot! Toot!
Honk! Honk!"
Then away it went!

It took Nick and Dick
and Father home.

The Toy Store

There was a little toy store
in the city.

It was on the street
with the big brown house.

The twins liked the toy store.

In the little toy store
was a storekeeper.
It was his toy store.
The storekeeper was Mr. Bangs.
He was the toy man,
and he lived in the toy store.

Mr. Bangs lived
in the toy store
with his little black dog, Fido.
Fido was so little that
he looked like a toy dog.

Mr. Bangs liked children.
He let the children
play with the toys in the store.

Fido liked children.
He said to the children,
"Bow-wow! Bow-wow!
Please play with me."

One morning Nick and Dick
came to the store
to buy a toy train.

Fido said,
"Bow-wow! Bow-wow!
Please play with me."

"The boys are going
to buy some toys, Fido,"
said Mr. Bangs.
"Then they will play with you."

The twins looked at the toys.
There were toy trains.
There were toy automobiles.
There were little red wagons.
There were toy horses
to draw the red wagons.

The twins looked and looked
at all the toys.

Then Dick said,
"I am going to buy
a toy train."

"Good!" said Nick.
"Then I am going to buy
a pretty little red wagon
with a horse to draw it."

Mr. Bangs put the toy train
in a yellow box.

He gave the box to Dick.

He put the little red wagon
and the horse in a black box.

He gave this box to Nick.

43

Then Nick and Dick
played with Fido.

The little black dog
ran up and down
and all around the toy store.
The twins ran with him.

Fido said,
"Bow-wow! Bow-wow!
It is fun to play!"

It was time to go home.
The twins said good-by
to Mr. Bangs.
They said good-by to Fido.

"Good-by, boys,"
said Mr. Bangs.

"Bow-wow! Bow-wow!
Come again," said Fido.

The Letter

One morning a letter
came for Father.
It was a letter
from Uncle David.

"Please read the letter!"
said Mother.

"Please read the letter!"
said the twins.

"Give me time," said Father.

The letter said,
"Please let Nick and Dick
come to see me.
They can have a good time
on the farm."

Father looked at the twins.
"Do you want to go, boys?"
he said.

"Yes," cried Nick and Dick.
"We want to see Uncle David."

"We want to see
the big farm," said Dick.

Mother packed suit-cases
for the twins.
Nick and Dick packed, too.

Mother and Father took
the twins to the train.

When it was time to go,
they all said,
"Good-by! Good-by!"

Then away went the train
to the farm.

Is This Right?

1. The twins went to the store with Mother.

2. Nick brought home the eggs.

3. Father let the twins buy some peanuts in the park.

4. Mr. Bangs lived at the toy store.

5. Mr. Bangs said, "Bow-wow! Bow-wow! Please play with me!"

6. One morning a letter came from Uncle David.

7. The twins went to the farm in a big green automobile.

CHAPTER THREE
The Farm

On the Train

The Twins and Uncle David

Uncle David met the twins
at the train.

He looked at Nick and Dick
and laughed.

"You look just alike!"
said Uncle David.

"I do not know
which twin is Nick,"
said Uncle David.
"I do not know
which twin is Dick."

Then the twins laughed!

"I do not know
which is which!"
said Uncle David.
"What can I do?"

"I am Nick. My tie is red,"
said the twin with the red tie.

"I am Dick. My tie is blue,"
said the twin with the blue tie.

54

"Red is for Nick!
Blue is for Dick!"
said Uncle David.
"That is how I can know
which boy is which,"
he said.

Uncle David's Automobile

"This is my automobile,"
said Uncle David.

Nick and Dick
got into the automobile.
Uncle David
got into the automobile.
Then away they went
to the farm.

Uncle David's House

Nick and Dick saw
a big white house.

They saw green grass
around the house.

They saw many trees
around the house.

"Look at all the grass,
and see the birds!" cried Nick.
"I can see five birds!"

"Look at all the trees!"
cried Dick.
"This is just like the park
at home."

Uncle David laughed.
"You can play in this park
every day," he said.

Maria

A woman came out
of the white house.
A big yellow cat
was with the woman.

"This is Maria,"
said Uncle David.

The twins said,
"How do you do, Maria?"

Uncle David said,
"Maria likes to make
good things to eat!"

Maria laughed and said,
"Yes, I do like to make
good things to eat."

"What do you like to eat?"
Maria said to the twins.

"I like cake!" said Nick.

"I like bread!" said Dick.

"I will make good bread
and good cake for you,"
said Maria.

The Yellow Cat

Uncle David took the twins
into the white house.

They saw a cat on the rug.
It was the big yellow cat
they had seen with Maria.
The twins ran to see the cat.

"What do you call the cat,
Uncle David?" said Nick.

"I call him Albert-Edward,"
said Uncle David.

"Mew-mew!"
said Albert-Edward.
"How do you do?"

"Albert-Edward sleeps
in a box," said Uncle David.

"Where do we sleep?"
said Dick.

"Come and see,"
said Uncle David.

The twins went
with Uncle David.
The yellow cat went, too.

"Do you know
where we are going to sleep,
Albert-Edward?" said Nick.

"Mew-mew,"
said Albert-Edward.

Twin Beds for Twins

There were little white beds
for Nick and Dick.

"Our beds are just alike.
They are twin beds,"
said Nick.

"Twin beds for twins!"
said Uncle David.

"Come to Supper!"

When they had seen the beds,
Maria called the twins
and Uncle David.

"Come to supper!" she called.

Nick and Dick
sat with Uncle David.
The yellow cat
sat on the rug.

Maria brought in the supper.
She brought bread and milk
for the twins.
She brought them
some little cakes, too.

The big cat said, "Mew-mew."
Then Maria brought milk
for Albert-Edward.

Going to Bed

It was night.
The twins went up to bed.
The yellow cat went with them.

"Albert-Edward wants
to sleep in my bed,"
called Nick.

"I will get his bed for him,"
said Uncle David.

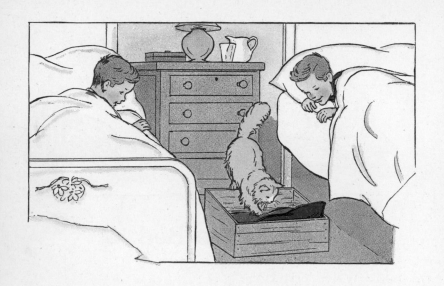

Uncle David put
Albert-Edward's box
by the white beds.

Albert-Edward saw his box.
He got into it
and went to sleep.

The twins went to sleep, too.

The Animals on the Farm

In the morning the twins
had a good breakfast.

After breakfast Uncle David
called to them.

"Come out!" he called.
"Come out and see
the animals on the farm!"

Uncle David
had many cows on his farm.
The cows were milked
by electricity.
That night the twins
saw the cows milked.

Uncle David had
many horses on his farm.
He took the twins
to see the horses.

Nick and Dick liked
the baby horses.
They liked to see them
run and play on the grass
under the trees.

"Oh, look at the big pigs!"
cried Nick.

There was a big white pig.
There were five
black and white pigs.

"Are there some baby pigs?"
said Dick.

"No," said Uncle David.

After they had seen the pigs,
Uncle David took the twins
to see the chickens.
They saw many white chickens.

The twins gave the chickens
some breakfast and some water.
They liked to see
the chickens drink water.

The Surprise

"I have a surprise
for you," said Uncle David.

"Where is the surprise?"
said Nick.

"The surprise
is in the biggest tree
on the farm,"
said Uncle David.
"The surprise is white."

Nick guessed that
the surprise was a white bird.
Dick guessed that
the surprise was a white cat.

"You have not guessed
the surprise,"
said Uncle David.
"It is not a bird.
It is not a cat.
Run and look
for the biggest tree
on the farm.
There you will see
the surprise."

The twins ran
to look at a big tree
by the white house.

It came up to the roof
of the white house.

"That tree is big,
but it is not the biggest tree
on the farm,"
said Uncle David.

76

The twins ran
to look at a big tree
in the barnyard.
It was bigger
than the big tree by the house.

"No, that is not
the biggest tree on the farm!"
said Uncle David.

Then the twins ran
back of the big red barn.
There they saw a big, big tree.
It was bigger than the big tree
in the barnyard.

"That is the biggest tree
on the farm!" cried the twins.

"Yes, it is!" said Uncle David.

The twins looked up
into the tree.
Oh, they were surprised!

"A house!" cried Nick.
"A house!" cried Dick.

Yes, there was a house
up in that big tree.
It was a little white house.

There were little white steps
going up to the house.
The house had a green door
and four windows.
It had a pretty red roof.

The twins were so surprised
when they saw the house
that they said, "Oh! Oh!
Oh! Oh! Oh! Oh!"

Uncle David laughed
to see how surprised they were.

"May we go into the house?"
said Dick.

Uncle David took the twins
into the little white house.
There was furniture
in the little house.
There was a blue rug.

The twins looked out
of the little windows.

"Is it all for us?"
cried Nick.

"Yes," said Uncle David.
"I made it all for you.
You can play in it every day."

"It is ours!" cried Nick.

"It is ours!" cried Dick.

The twins laughed
and laughed and laughed!
They hopped up and down!
Uncle David laughed, too.

After they had hopped
up and down
three or four times,
Nick and Dick said,
"This is a good surprise,
Uncle David. Thank you,
thank you for our little house
in the tree!"

What Am I?

1.

I am big and white.

I have green grass around me.

Maria lives in me.

Albert-Edward lives in me.

What am I?

2.

I am little and white.

I have white steps.

I have a green door.

I have four windows.

I have a red roof.

I have some furniture.

What am I?

CHAPTER FOUR
Fun at the Farm

85

The New Farmers

The New Farmers

Uncle David gave Nick
a suit of new red over-alls.
He gave Dick a suit
of new blue over-alls.
The twins
put on the over-alls.

"Now you are farmers,"
said Uncle David.

"Let us do things to help you,
Uncle David," said Nick.

"There are many things
to do on a big farm,"
said Uncle David.
"I have four men here now
to help me."

"Nick and I are farmers, too,"
said Dick.
"We want to do the things
that farmers do."

Uncle David laughed.
"I will call you
my two new farmers," he said.

Every morning
the new farmers went out
to look for eggs.

They brought the eggs
to Uncle David.

He packed them into big boxes.

He let the boys help him.

The boxes of eggs
were to go to the city.

Every night the new farmers
saw the cows milked
by electricity.

Some of the milk
was put into big cans.
Uncle David sent milk
to the city every day.
He sent eggs to the city, too.

One of Uncle David's men
took the milk and eggs
to the train.

The man let Nick and Dick
ride with him.

It was fun to ride
so early in the morning.

The twins liked to see
the milk and the eggs
put on the train.

The twins had time
to play, too.

Every day they went
to the tree house.

They went there
right after dinner,
and the yellow cat
went with them.

Night on the Farm

At night all the animals
came home to their barns.

Uncle David and his men
gave them their supper.

The cows were milked
in the barn.

They had supper in the barn, too.

The horses stopped
in the barnyard
for a drink of water.
Then they walked
into their barn for supper.

The pigs and chickens
had their supper, too.
Then it was bed-time
for the animals.

Betty and Bobby

Betty and Bobby
lived on a farm.
Their home was not far
from Uncle David's farm.

One day they rode
to Uncle David's farm.
They rode on horses.

Uncle David met the children.
They hopped down
from their horses.
Uncle David said to them,
"Come and see the twins."

He and Betty and Bobby
walked to the tree house.
Then he called to the twins.
"Here are some new friends
for you!"

"Come up and see
our tree house," said Dick.
"Uncle David made it."

"Come up and play," said Nick.

Betty and Bobby
liked the little tree house.

"What a pretty little house!"
cried Betty.
"Oh, Bobby, see the furniture
and the little green door!"

"It is fun to be away up
in a tree!" said Bobby.

Maria came to the little house.
She brought cakes and milk
and some cups for the milk.
Albert-Edward came, too.
He came to play
and to get some of the milk!

The children played and played.
They had a good time.
Then Betty and Bobby went home.

Going to the County Fair

One morning
the twins got up early.
They were going
to the County Fair.

They were going
with Uncle David.
Maria was going, too.
Albert-Edward was not going.
He did not want to go.

On the way to the Fair
Uncle David stopped
the automobile.
He stopped at a farm house.

"I have a surprise for you,"
he said to Nick and Dick.
"Betty and Bobby
are going to the Fair with us."

"What fun!" cried the twins.

The Merry-Go-Round

There were many things
to see at the County Fair.
The children did not know
what to look at first!

"Oh, let us ride
on the merry-go-round!"
cried Nick.

All the children ran
to the merry-go-round.

101

Around and around
went the merry-go-round!
The children rode
again and again.

Nick and Dick rode
on black horses or blue horses.
Betty and Bobby rode
on red horses or yellow horses.

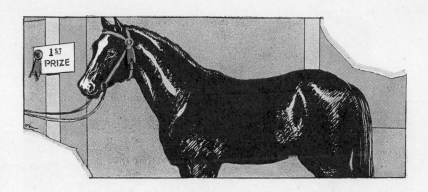

The Prize Animals

Uncle David took the twins
and Betty and Bobby
to see the prize animals.

They saw a big black horse.
It was a pretty horse.
It had on a blue ribbon.
"That black horse
got the first prize!"
said Uncle David.

"Here is the cow
that got the first prize!"
cried Betty.

The children ran to look
at the prize cow.
She had a blue ribbon, too.
She was a big cow.
She was brown and white.

Dinner at the Fair

"It is time for dinner,"
said Maria.

Uncle David took a big box
from the automobile.
Maria opened the box.
She took out good things to eat
and a bottle of milk and cups.

They all sat down
on the grass to eat dinner.

A woman came and said,
"Do you want ice-cream?"

"Yes," said Uncle David,
"this is a warm day.
We will all have ice-cream!"

"I like ice-cream," said Nick.

"So do I," said Betty
and Dick and Bobby.

A Surprise for Uncle David

"Come with us!"
said the twins to Maria.
"We are going to buy
a surprise for Uncle David."

"What is it?" said Maria.

"A baby pig!" said Nick.
"A little baby pig," said Dick.

The twins took Maria
to the man with the baby pigs.
"That pig looks like
a good one!" said Nick.

"Yes, I want that one!"
said Dick.

The man put the little pig
into a box.

The twins took the box
to Uncle David.

"Here is a surprise for you!"
they said.

Uncle David opened the box.
He was surprised.

"A baby pig for me!" he cried.
"Thank you, boys, thank you!"

"This pig is so little
that he can have only milk,"
said Bobby.

"I will give him milk
every morning," said Nick.

"I will give him milk
every night," said Dick.

"I will give him milk, too,"
said Maria.

"When he gets bigger,"
said Uncle David,
"he can live with the pigs
in the barn.
But he is too little now."

"It is time to go home,"
said Uncle David.

"It is time for the pig
to go to bed," said Maria.

The twins and Betty and Bobby
got into the automobile.
They went to sleep
on the way home.
So did the baby pig.

110

Do You Know?

1. Who sent milk to the city?
2. Who packed the eggs in boxes?
3. Who rode in the truck?
4. Who saw cows milked
by electricity?
5. Who were the new friends?
6. Who said, "It is fun
to be away up in a tree!"?
7. Who went to the County Fair?
8. Who rode
on the merry-go-round?
9. What had blue ribbons?
10. Who gave Uncle David
a surprise?

Draw a Big Picture

Draw a big picture
of the County Fair.

Put a merry-go-round
in the picture.

Draw a woman with ice-cream
for people to buy.

Put the man with baby pigs
in the picture.

Draw the prize animals
at the Fair.

Can you put Uncle David
and Maria and the twins
and Betty and Bobby
into the picture?

CHAPTER FIVE
Home and School

The Letter

114

A Letter from Home

One day the twins
and Betty and Bobby
were playing in the tree house.

Albert-Edward, the yellow cat,
was playing with them.

Uncle David came
to the tree house.

"Here is a letter for you,"
he said to the twins.

The twins opened their letter.
"It is from Mother,"
said Nick.
"Please read it, Uncle David."

The letter said,
"It is time for you
to come home.
It is time for you
to go to school."

"But I do not want you
to go!" cried Betty.

"They will come back, Betty,"
said Uncle David.

"Yes, we will come back,"
said the twins.
"We love the farm
and Uncle David."

"The tree house will be here
when you come back,"
said Uncle David.
"Maria will be here.
Albert-Edward will be here.
I will be here."

Betty and Bobby
were going home.

The twins said good-by
to them that day.

Betty and Bobby
said good-by to the twins.

They all said good-by
under the tree house.

Good-By to the Farm!

Early in the morning
the twins said good-by
to the little house in the tree.

They said good-by
to Uncle David's four men.

They said good-by
to the cows and the horses.
They said good-by
to the pigs and the chickens.
They said good-by
to the little pig that came
from the Fair.
He was bigger now
than when he was at the Fair.

The twins said good-by
to Albert-Edward, the yellow cat.

They said, "Thank you, Maria,
for all the good things to eat
and all the cups of milk.
Good-by!"

Uncle David took the twins
to the train in his automobile.
He took their suit-cases.

The train stopped.
The twins got on the train.
A man took their suit-cases
for them.

"Good-by, Uncle David!"
they cried.
"We had a good time!
We love the farm!"

"Choo! Choo! Choo! Choo!"
said the train.
Then away it went to the city.

Home Again

Mother and Father
met the twins at the train.

"How brown you look!"
cried Mother.

"They have played
in the sun every day,"
said Father.
"That has made them brown."

Going to School

One morning
Nick and Dick got up early.
They were going to school.
The school was not far away.

"This is the first day
of school," said Father.
"You know the way,
but I will walk to school
with you this morning."

Nick and Dick
were in the First Grade.

There were many boys and girls
in the First Grade,
but Nick and Dick
were the only twins.

The twins liked school.
They liked the boys and girls.
They liked the teacher.
They liked their new books.

Nick looked at the pictures
in his book.
Dick looked at the pictures
in his book.

Playing on the Roof

The First Grade teacher
was Miss Wood.

Every morning Miss Wood
took the children out to play.

She took them up to the roof
of the school.

It was fun to play
up on the roof in the warm sun.

When the children came back,
they had milk to drink.

The milk was not in cups.
It was in little bottles.
The First Grade children liked
to drink their milk
out of the little bottles.

The Subway

One day Miss Wood said,
"We are going to the Zoo,
this morning.
We are going to see
the animals at the Zoo.
The Zoo is far away.
We cannot walk there.
We will go on a subway train."

A new little girl said,
"What is a subway train?"

"A subway train is a train
that runs under the streets,"
said the teacher.
"You have to go down,
down, down many steps
to get to the subway."

Miss Wood and the children
came away from school.
They walked a little way.
They went down some steps.
They got into the subway train.
Away it went—
faster and faster and faster.

It stopped many times.
People got on
when the train stopped.
Then away it went again,
faster and faster.

A stop came and a man called,
"All out for the Zoo!"

At the Zoo

When they came to the Zoo,
the boys and girls ran
to look at the lions.

A mother lion was playing
with two little ones.

The father lion looked out
and gave a big roar.

The big roar
surprised the children.

"There is a tiger!
He looks like a big cat,"
said Nick.

The tiger had yellow stripes
and black stripes
on his back.
He walked up and down,
up and down, up and down.
He did not stop at all.
He did not roar.

132

"May we look at the snakes?"
said Dick.

"Oh, no! I do not want
to see the snakes,"
said one of the girls.

But they went with Miss Wood
to see the snakes.
There were big snakes
and little ones,
all curled up.

"Snakes like to sleep,"
said one of the boys.

"They like to sleep
all curled up," said Nick.

133

The children
saw all the animals.

Then they went back to school.

"It is fun to live
in the city," said Nick.
"There are so many things
to see in the city."

"There are many things to see
on a farm, too," said Dick.
"I like the farm."

Who Said It?

1. "We love the farm."
2. "They were playing
in the sun every day."
3. "I will walk to school
with you."
4. "Snakes like to sleep."

Is This Right?

1. The lions were all curled up.
2. The subway train did not stop.
3. The sun on the roof was warm.
4. Nick and Dick
were the only twins
in the First Grade.
5. A tiger has stripes.

WORD LIST

This word list contains all the new words—286 in number—occurring in *Nick and Dick*. Derivatives are counted as new words, except that such singular and plural forms as *boy* and *boys* or *runs* and *run* are counted as one word. Omitting proper names, the count is 275. Of these 275 words, 95 per cent are in the Gates word list for primary grades and 89 per cent are in the first 2000 of the Thorndike word list.

The list includes 220 words that are used in the Work-Play Books Primer, *Peter and Peggy*.

The words are grouped under the numbers of the pages on which they first appear.

1	9	17	27
chapter	at	which	brought
one	top	right	home
in	of	**18**	then
the	down	—	were
city	**10**	**19**	**28**
2	can	two	park
Nick	see	**20**	please
and	automobiles	store	father
Dick	people	**21**	will
3	**11**	am	**29**
twins	go	said	rode
boys	up	mother	bus
are	honk	may	sat
4	toot	**22**	high
look	**12**	yes	**30**
just	there	you	from
alike	green	went	grass
5	lights	**23**	**31**
has	for	was	had
a	**13**	policeman	dinner
red	says	good	box
suit	to	morning	eat
6	stop	**24**	**32**
blue	**14**	we	balloon
this	elevator	cross	man
is	ride	when	let
7	**15**	saw	pretty
street	Ben	**25**	**33**
live	he	storekeeper	looked
on	likes	what	peanut
8	give	buy	**34**
big	**16**	**26**	played
brown	I	some	ran
house	going	milk	with
they	it	bread	
	fun	eggs	

35
time
away
took

36
toy
little
liked

37
his
Mr.
 Bangs
lived

38
black
dog
Fido
so

39
children
play
bow-wow
me

40
came
train

41
wagons
horses
draw

42
all

43
put
yellow
gave

44
around
him

45
good-by
come
again

46
letter
Uncle
 David
read

47
have
farm

48
do
want
cried

49
packed
suit-cases
too

50
—

51
three

52
—

53
met
laughed

54
not
know
my
tie

55
that
how

56
David's
got
into

57
white
many
trees

58
five
birds
every
day

59
Maria
woman
out
cat

60
make
things
cake

61
rug

62
call
Albert-Edward
mew-mew

63
sleeps
where

64
beds
our

65
supper
called
she

66
them

67
night
get

68
by

69
animals
breakfast
after

70
cows
milked
electricity

71
baby
run
under

72
oh
pigs
no

73
chickens
water

74
surprise

biggest
guessed

75
—

76
roof
but

77
barnyard
bigger
than

78
back
barn
surprised

79
—

80
steps
door
windows

81
furniture

82
us
made
hopped

83
or
four
thank

84
—

85
—

86
new
farmers

87
over-alls
now

88
men
here
help

89
boxes

90
sent
91
early
92
—
93
their
94
stopped
drink
walked
95
Betty
Bobby
far
96
friends
97
be
98
cups
99
county
fair
did
way
100
—

101
merry-go-round
first
102
—
103
prize
ribbon
104
—
105
bottle
106
ice-cream
warm
107
—
108
opened
109
only
110
—
111
who
112
picture

113
school
114
—
115
playing
116
—
117
love
118
—
119
—
120
—
121
choo
122
sun
123
walk
124
grade
girls
125
teacher
books

126
Miss
Wood
127
—
128
zoo
subway
129
faster
130
—
131
lion
roar
132
tiger
stripes
133
snakes
curled
134
—
135
—